William Shakespeare
The Winter's Tale

Retold by
Marcia Williams

WALKER
BOOKS

William Shakespeare
The Winter's Tale

First published 2015 by Walker Books Ltd
87 Vauxhall Walk, London SE11 5HJ

2 4 6 8 10 9 7 5 3 1

This book has been typeset in Kennerly Regular

Printed and bound in Germany

British Library Cataloguing in Publication Data:
a catalogue record for this book is available from the British Library

ISBN 978-1-4063-6431-6

www.walker.co.uk

For Mathilda

Contents

In which Leontes is
consumed with jealousy.
Page 7

In which a baby is born.
Page 16

In which the king's jealousy
has tragic consequences.
Page 24

In which astonishing
discoveries are made.
Page 29

In which Paulina finds happiness.
Page 43

William Shakespeare
Page 46

Marcia Williams
Page 47

In which Leontes is consumed with jealousy.

King Leontes of Sicily was feeling grumpy –
there was too much bustle at court.

His beloved wife, Queen Hermione,
was expecting their second child any day
now, so all her ladies were rushing around
in high excitement; their young son, Prince
Mamillius, was entertaining everyone with
his most exciting tales; and Leontes' good
friend, King Polixenes, was preparing to

return to his own kingdom of Bohemia.

Polixenes was Leontes' oldest and dearest friend, and he had been staying with Leontes for the past nine months. It had been a grand time and the two men had delighted in sharing childhood memories, but now Polixenes was eager to depart. The winter weather was closing in, and he was

missing his own son, Prince Florizel.

Polixenes hugged his friend warmly and thanked him for his hospitality.

"Stay your thanks a while; and pay them when you part," replied Leontes, shrugging his friend off.

"Sir, that's tomorrow," smiled Polixenes.

Leontes did not return the smile. He had

tried and failed to persuade his old friend to stay. In a final effort to get Polixenes to change his plans, he asked Queen Hermione to persuade Polixenes to delay his departure.

To please her husband, Hermione used all her feminine wiles to cajole Polixenes into staying. Finally she succeeded. "He'll stay, my lord," she cried triumphantly.

"At my request he would not," replied Leontes, feeling a sudden rush of jealousy.

Hermione laughed at her husband's

ungracious response and gave Polixenes
her hand in gratitude.

Leontes fixed his eyes upon their
linked hands and his heart began to
thunder against his chest. "My heart
dances; but not for joy," he muttered
to himself. He stomped off, leaving
Hermione to entertain his friend.

"He something seems unsettled," said
Hermione, hoping that his mood would
pass if he was left to himself.

However, the jealousy that had taken hold of Leontes was not shifted that easily.

Faster and louder beat his heart, until it had driven all sane thoughts from his head. His wife had never shown herself to be anything but loving and faithful, and Polixenes was like a brother to him, yet Leontes was now convinced that the pair were in love.

In a state of rage, he went to see Lord Camillo, his friend and advisor. "My wife is slippery," he informed him.

"Good my lord, be cured of this diseased opinion, for 'tis most dangerous," Camillo cried.

"Say it be, 'tis true," said the king, furious that Camillo dared to argue with him.

"No, no, my lord," said Camillo, who was certain Queen Hermione loved Leontes.

"It is; you lie, you lie," cried Leontes, beside himself with anger and jealousy. "I say thou liest, Camillo, and I hate thee."

Camillo was shocked by Leontes' fury – but there was something more shocking to come: Leontes asked him to poison a cup and kill Polixenes. The king grabbed

Camillo's jacket and held him close. "Do't, and thou hast the one half of my heart," he promised. "Do't not, thou split'st thine own."

Camillo was left shaken and trembling by this terrible request. Could Leontes be serious? If so, must Camillo obey his king's command and murder an innocent man? For Camillo did not doubt that King Polixenes was innocent.

Camillo decided to tell Polixenes of Leontes' wicked plan and flee with him to Bohemia that very night. Leontes seemed to have been struck by a terrible disease of the mind, but Camillo was sure he would soon recover. Then he would be able to return to Sicily.

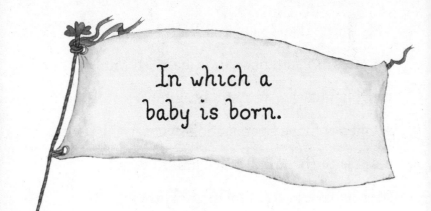

In which a
baby is born.

The whole court soon became aware
of the king's anger. Hermione was
confused and hurt by her husband's
sudden coldness and took comfort in
her little son, Mamillius. She sat with
him in front of a warm fire while he
tried to think up an exciting story to
distract her.

"A sad tale's best for winter," he said,

stroking her hand. "I have one of sprites
and goblins."

"Let's have that, good sir," smiled his
mother sadly.

"There was a man," said Mamillius,
in a ghostly whisper, "dwelt by a
churchyard—"

But Mamillius never got any further
with his tale, for at that moment his father

burst through the door, followed by his
armed guards.

"Bear the boy hence; he shall not come
about her," Leontes ordered, determined
that Hermione should have nothing more
to do with the young prince. "Away with
her to prison!"

Mamillius cried out for his mother,
but Leontes was unmoved. Camillo and
Polixenes had escaped earlier that night,

and he was now convinced that they and Queen Hermione were plotting to murder him!

Hermione bore all this with quiet dignity, sure that her husband would soon return to his senses. She asked only that she might take her ladies and her friend Paulina to prison with her, for her baby was about to be born.

The rest of the court looked on in horror at these events.

"Be certain what you do, sir, lest your justice prove violence," one lord dared to say.

"Beseech your highness call the queen again," begged another.

But Leontes just grew angrier. "Hold your peaces!" he yelled.

Mamillius was heartbroken to think of his adored mother in jail and refused to eat. Day after day the prince grew weaker, but still Leontes would not repent. He was determined to bring his wife to court and see her sentenced to death. Hoping to silence the many courtiers who doubted his wife's guilt, he sent two lords to consult the Oracle at Delphi in Greece.

Meanwhile, in prison, Hermione gave
birth to a daughter, Perdita. Her friend
Paulina, in a bid to soften Leontes' heart,
wrapped the baby in Hermione's favourite
shawl, fixed it with one of her brooches
and presented her to Leontes.

"The good queen, for she is good," said
brave Paulina, "hath brought you forth
a daughter: here 'tis; commends it to your
blessing."

"Out!" yelled Leontes furiously. "A

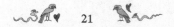

mankind witch! Hence with her, out o' door!"

"I pray you, do not push me: I'll be gone,"
said Paulina. "Look to your babe, my lord;
'tis yours."

Paulina left little Perdita at the king's
feet. Leontes looked down on the infant
with loathing, convinced that she was not
his child, but Polixenes'.

"This brat is none of mine. Take it up.
I'll not rear another's issue," he yelled at
Antigonus, Paulina's husband. He ordered

him to take Perdita and set sail for some
foreign shore, and there abandon Perdita
to her fate.

"Come on, poor babe," crooned Antigonus,
as he lifted Perdita into his arms and carried
her away from the king's wrath.

In which the king's jealousy has tragic consequences.

Leontes decided he would not wait to hear what the Oracle decreed and he ordered Hermione's trial to start at once. Hermione entered the court with her ladies and her friend Paulina, her head held high. As soon as the court sat and the session began, the two messengers returned from Delphi. After swearing that the Oracle had not been tampered with, one of the lords

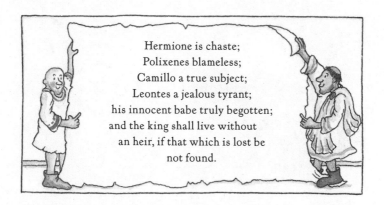

Hermione is chaste;
Polixenes blameless;
Camillo a true subject;
Leontes a jealous tyrant;
his innocent babe truly begotten;
and the king shall live without
an heir, if that which is lost be
not found.

read out its secrets to the court.

"Hermione is chaste; Polixenes blameless; Camillo a true subject; Leontes a jealous tyrant; his innocent babe truly begotten; and the king shall live without an heir, if that which is lost be not found."

The Oracle had proclaimed Hermione innocent!

"Now blessed be the great Apollo!" cried the whole court – apart from Leontes.

"There is no truth at all i' the Oracle; the

sessions shall proceed," he ordered.

Then all of a sudden, a servant ran into
the courtroom. He had terrible news
to report: Mamillius, overwhelmed by
sorrow, had suddenly died. A gasp of
horror went round the court and
Hermione collapsed to the floor.

"This news is mortal to the queen,"
sobbed Paulina, as she helped to carry
Hermione from the courtroom.

Suddenly Leontes' madness seemed
to leave him, and he woke to the terrible

harm his wicked jealousy had caused.

"Apollo's angry; and the heavens themselves do strike at my injustice," he cried. He fell to his knees and begged Apollo for forgiveness. But his repentance

came too late, for Paulina returned to tell him that Hermione had

also died. Her poor heart had been unable
to take the pain of losing her two children
and her husband's love. Paulina railed against

Leontes in
her misery.

The king
was desolate
and deeply
ashamed, and

he took every angry word that Paulina threw
at him as his due punishment. He swore to
her that he would live a life of mourning.

"Will you swear never to marry but by my
free leave?" shouted Paulina.

"Never, Paulina: so be bless'd my spirit,"
spirit," he swore.

In which astonishing discoveries are made.

Meanwhile, out at sea, a storm had hit
the ship carrying Antigonus and Perdita
and driven it onto the shores of Bohemia.
The ship and all its crew were lost to the
rocks and the raging sea, but Antigonus
managed to wade ashore with Perdita safe in
his arms, still wrapped in Hermione's shawl.
As the rain lashed at his face, he found
shelter for this tiny bundle between two
rocks. There he left Perdita to her fate.

He turned back towards the sea, hoping
to find a ship that would take him back
to Sicily – but as he slipped and scrambled
across the rocks, a huge bear reared up at
him out of the darkness. Poor Antigonus
was never heard of again.

Luckily, Perdita was found by a
shepherd who was out looking for lost
sheep. He took her home to his wife,
and they cared for her as a daughter
for the next fifteen years.

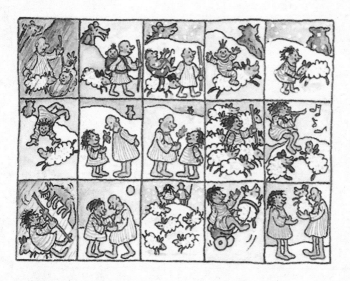

Perdita grew into a beautiful young woman, and although she was brought up as a shepherdess, she had all the natural charm and grace of a princess. Indeed, when Prince Florizel, son of King Polixenes, met her whilst out hunting, he fell in love with her in an instant.

"I bless the time when my good falcon made her flight across thy father's ground," he

he said to Perdita. For if it hadn't been for the falcon, how would a prince ever have met and fallen in love with a shepherd's daughter?

Lord Camillo, who was living with Florizel and King Polixenes at their palace, would have been astonished if he had known that his old friend King Leontes' daughter was living as a shepherdess just

a few miles from the palace. Camillo longed
to return to Sicily – he had heard that
Leontes had recovered from his madness and
now lived a quiet and gentle life. However,
King Polixenes would not hear of Camillo
leaving, for he had come to rely on his advice.
Indeed, when Polixenes heard rumours that
his son was courting a lowly shepherd's
daughter, he turned at once to Camillo. He
wanted to meet Perdita for himself, and
wanted Camillo to go with him.

The two men disguised themselves as peasants and set off for Perdita's home. There they found Florizel and Perdita, and were astonished to be asked to witness their engagement. So complete were their disguises that Florizel hadn't even recognized his own father. King Polixenes was outraged that his son should become engaged to a shepherd's daughter – and without his permission! He threw off his hat and false beard and angrily forbade the engagement. "Thou art too base

to be acknowledg'd," he cried to his son. "Follow us to the court."

But Camillo was charmed by the two young lovers and thought he might use their love to his advantage. As soon as King Polixenes was out of earshot, he persuaded them to escape to Sicily and beg King Leontes' support for their marriage. He felt sure that Leontes would not refuse to help the son of his old friend Polixenes. "Methinks I see Leontes opening

his free arms and weeping his welcomes
forth," he assured them.

Camillo hoped that once Florizel and
Perdita were safely aboard a ship to Sicily,
he would be able to bring Polixenes around
to the idea of the marriage and follow the
pair back to his beloved homeland.

So the two lovers travelled to Sicily,
accompanied by the shepherd. As Camillo
had predicted, King Leontes welcomed
Prince Florizel to his court with open arms,

crying, "Most dearly welcome! And your fair princess – goddess!"

Leontes could not stop staring at Perdita – she looked exactly like his lost wife. Sad memories came flooding back to him, and he told his guests how he had caused the deaths of his wife and son, and sent his daughter away.

As King Leontes talked, it dawned on the shepherd that Perdita could be Leontes' daughter. At first no one could believe this possible, but finally all agreed it must be so. Many rumours flew about the court as to how it was proved. One gentleman swore the baby was found with the mantle of Queen Hermione. "Methought I heard the shepherd say he found the child," whispered another.

Leontes was overcome with happiness. "The Oracle is fulfilled," everyone agreed.

Perdita wanted to know what her mother

had looked like, so Paulina agreed to show her a statue of the queen, which she kept at her house. When she drew the curtain from around the statue, the princess and her father gasped – Hermione looked so lifelike, and so very like Perdita.

"Chide me, dear stone, that I may say indeed thou art Hermione," the king whispered in wonder.

He could not take his eyes off the statue.
The sculptor must have been most talented,
he thought, for this statue showed Hermione
as she might have looked that very day, older
than when husband and wife had last met.
"Hermione was not so much wrinkled," he
remarked.

Paulina smiled and called for music.

To everyone's amazement, the statue began to move. Slowly, as though waking from a long dream, Hermione – for it was really her – descended the pedestal and embraced Leontes.

"O, she's warm!" he sighed. "If this be magic, let it be an art lawful as eating."

Hermione had always kept faith in the

Oracle. Believing that one day Perdita would be found, she waited in secret, walking like a ghost through the castle, hoping for this moment. Now, after so many years of loneliness, she was reunited with both her husband and her daughter.

In which Paulina
finds happiness.

When King Polixenes arrived and
discovered his son's shepherdess was
actually a princess, he gave his blessing
for Florizel and Perdita's marriage. So
the two families were joined in harmony
once more.

Only Paulina, who had helped bring
about this happiness, was dissatisfied,
for her husband had never returned from

his encounter with the bear on the shores
of Bohemia.

"I, an old turtle, will wing me to some
wither'd bough and there my mate, that's
never to be found again, lament till I am
lost," she grumped.

"O, peace, Paulina!" laughed Leontes.
"Thou shouldst a husband take. Come,
Camillo..."

He gave Paulina's hand in marriage
to Camillo, for they had long held each
other in deep affection.

So ended the strange story of how Paulina
kept Hermione hidden and how Perdita was
found – a wonderful winter's tale to tell by
the fireside. For although the tale is tinged
with sadness, as poor Prince Mamillius once
said, "A sad tale's best for winter."

WILLIAM SHAKESPEARE was a popular playwright, poet and actor who lived in Elizabethan England. He married in Stratford-upon-Avon aged eighteen and had three children, although one died in childhood. Shakespeare then moved to London, where he wrote 39 plays and over 150 sonnets, many of which are still very popular today. In fact, his plays are performed more often than those of any other playwright, and he died 450 years ago! His gravestone includes a curse against interfering with his burial place, possibly to deter people from opening it in search of unpublished manuscripts. It reads, "Blessed be the man that spares these stones, and cursed be he that moves my bones." Spooky!

MARCIA WILLIAMS' mother was a novelist and her father a playwright, so it's not surprising that Marcia ended up an author herself. Although she never trained formally as an artist, she found that motherhood, and the time she spent later as a nursery school teacher, inspired her to start writing and illustrating children's books.

Marcia's books bring to life some of the world's all-time favourite stories and some colourful historical characters. Her hilarious retellings and clever observations will have children laughing out loud and coming back for more!

More retellings from Marcia Williams

ISBN 978-1-4063-5692-2

ISBN 978-1-4063-5693-9

ISBN 978-1-4063-5694-6

ISBN 978-1-4063-5695-3

Available from all good booksellers

www.walker.co.uk